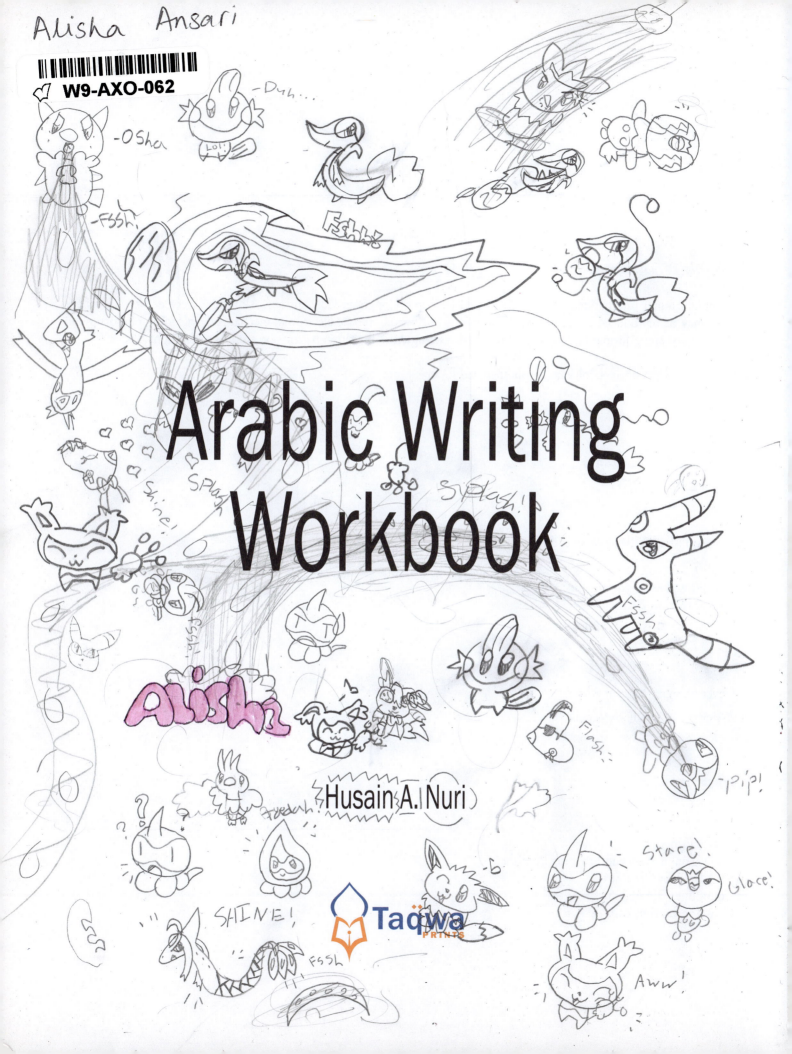

Arabic Writing Workbook

Husain A. Nuri

ISBN: 978-1-936569-14-4

First published 2010 by Weekend Learning Publishers

First printed as a Taqwa Prints: 2012
Second reprint: 2013

Cover Design: Mansur Ahmad
Typesetting: Lenni Nazir

Printed in China

Taqwa Prints
A Division of Weekend Learning Publishers
5584 Boulder Crest St.
Columbus, OH 43235
www.Taqwaprints.com

Parent, Teacher Guide

Early start is a good start. When your child is about ready to hold a pencil and draw a square, a curve, a circle and a straight line, he or she is ready to start writing alphabets. While a regular school will work on developing English writing skills, as a parent and an Islamic school teacher, you should help your child develop Arabic writing skills.

Most students will learn writing Arabic letters and small words by the time they are five to six years of age.

For each page, your child should practice writing the letters and small words. Do not push him/her to write too many of the same letter or word. Do not push him/her to the point of frustration. Take it easy with them but at the same time encourage them to learn and remember. In the first half of the book, after every few pages, there is a review page to check the progress and reinforce learning.

 This workbook is not intended to teach tajweed rules. The placement and significance of different vowel marks have intricate rules. These rules should be learned with the help of a teacher who is qualified to teach tajweed.

When you are working with your child, make sure he or she is enjoying the exercise. Make his or her learning time fun, secure and rewarding. Remember, in the beginning your child may not be able to write perfect shapes of the letters. A word of genuine and specific praise will encourage the child.

Remember, proper posture and paper placement will help your child write more correctly and clearly. Below are the paper positions recommended in most writing programs.

Right-handed paper placement

Left-Handed paper placement

Learning complete alphabet

Let us learn the complete Arabic alphabet. After we learn them, next we will practice writing them.

ج	ث	ت	ب	أ
ر	ذ	د	خ	ح
ض	ص	ش	س	ز
ف	غ	ظ	ع	ط
ن	م	ل	ك	ق
	ي	و	هـ	

Learning lines and curves

Look at the arrows. Trace each lines and curves along the dotted lines in the direction of the arrow. Writing skills developed through this exercise will help when we begin writing the letters.

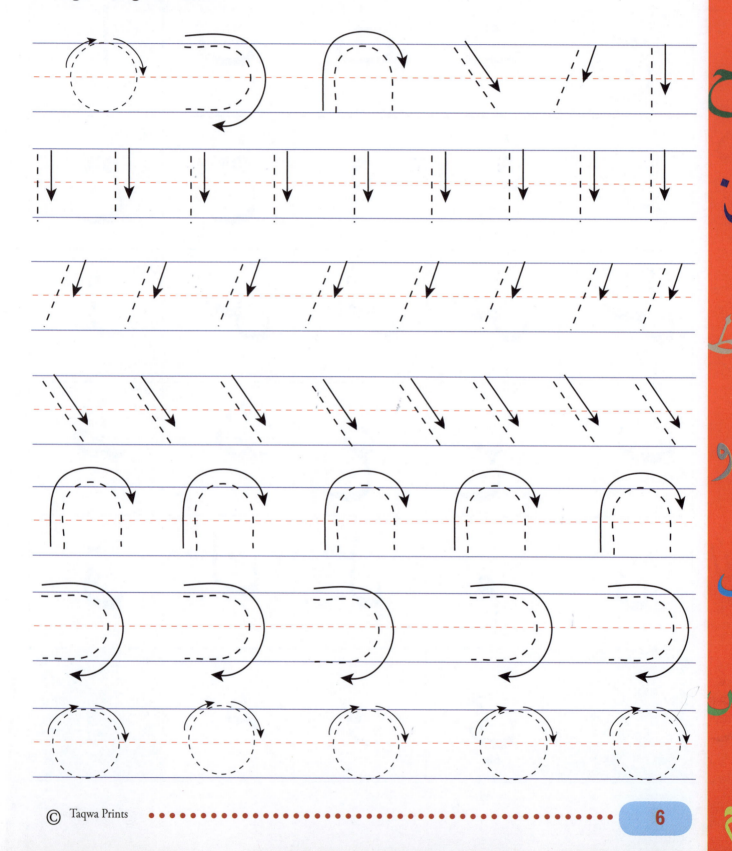

Learning letter Alif

Look at the arrows. Trace each letter in the direction of the arrow. Next, write the letter on the blank lines. Note, the letter Alif is written above the red dashed line. It has a hamza sign on top of it. We will practice writing both the signs.

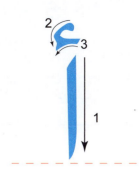

Learning letter Ba

Look at the arrows. Trace each letter starting with the Number 1 arrow, continuing with number 2 arrow and so on. Do not lift your pencil while writing along the arrows. Then put a dot below the letter. Next, write the letter on the blank lines.

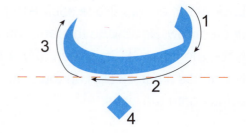

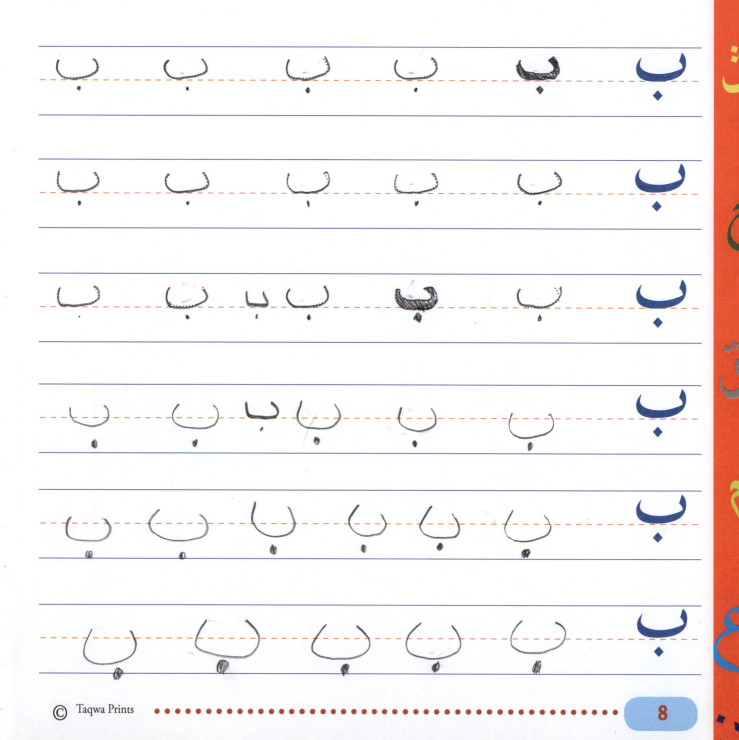

Learning letter Taa

Look at the arrows. Trace each letter starting with the Number 1 arrow, continuing with number 2 arrow and so on. Do not lift your pencil while writing along the arrows. Then put two dots above the letter. Next, write the letter on the blank lines.

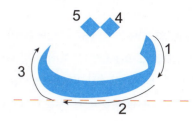

© Taqwa Prints

Learning letter Thaa

Look at the arrows. Trace each letter starting with the Number 1 arrow, continuing with number 2 arrow and so on. Do not lift your pencil while writing along the arrows. Then put three dots above the letter. Next, write the letter on the blank lines.

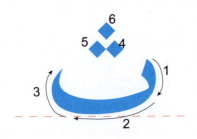

Practice letters

أ إ إ إ إ أ

ب ﺑ ﺑ ﺑ ﺑ

ت ﺗ ﺗ ﺗ ﺗ ﺗ

ث ﺛ ﺛ ﺛ ﺛ ﺛ

أ أ أ أ ا

ب ﺑ ﺑ ﺑ ﺑ

ت ﺗ ﺗ ﺗ ﺗ

ث ﺛ ﺛ ﺛ ﺛ

Learning letter Jeem

Look at the arrows. Trace each letter starting with the Number 1 arrow, continuing with number 2 arrow. Do not lift your pencil while writing along the arrows. Then put a dot in the center as shown. Next, write the letter on the blank lines.

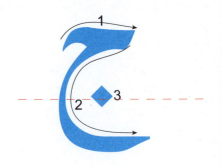

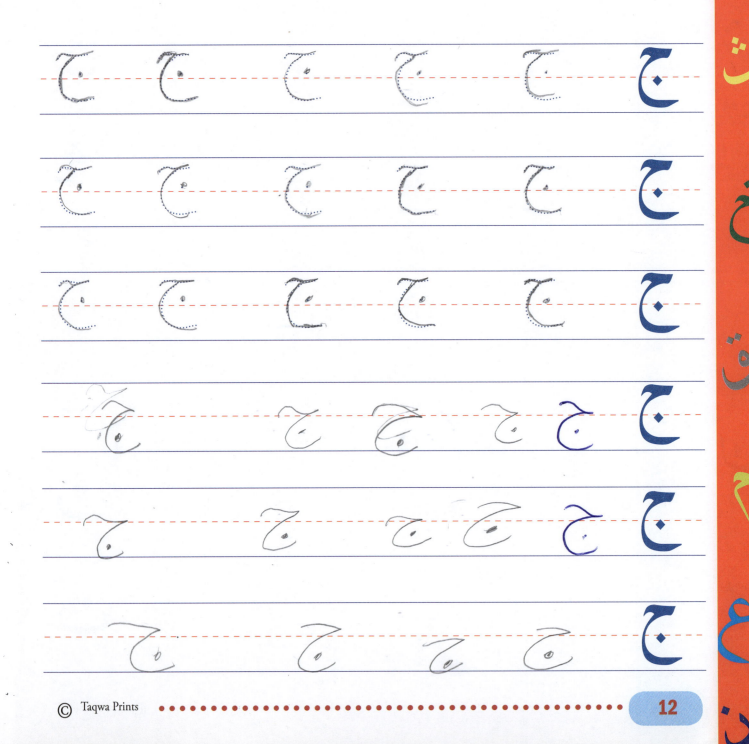

Learning letter Haa

Look at the arrows. Trace each letter starting with the Number 1 arrow, continuing with number 2 arrow. Do not lift your pencil while writing along the arrows. No dots are needed in this letter. Next, write the letter on the blank lines.

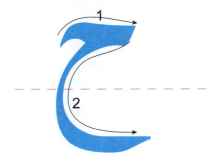

Learning letter Khaa

Look at the arrows. Trace each letter starting with the Number 1 arrow, continuing with number 2 arrow. Do not lift your pencil while writing along the arrows. Then put a dot above the letter as shown. Next, write the letter on the blank lines.

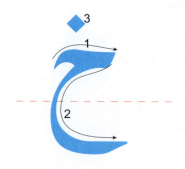

Practice letters

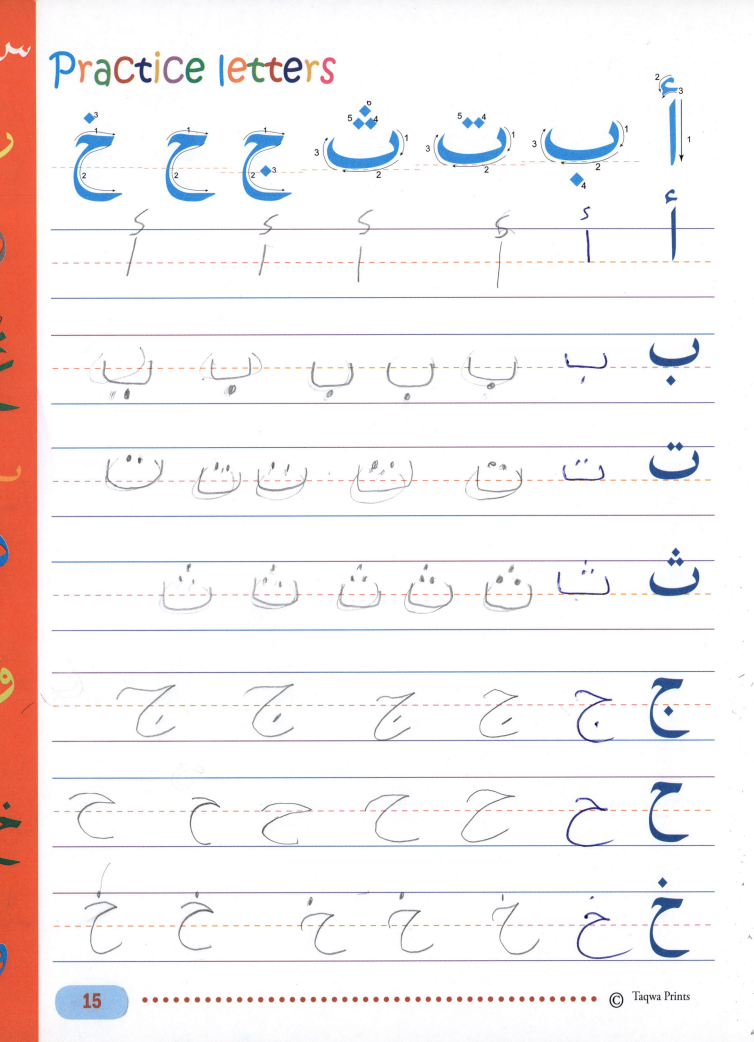

© Taqwa Prints

Learning letter Daal

Look at the arrows. Trace each letter in the direction of the arrow. Next, write the letter on the blank lines. Note, the letter Daal is written above the red dashed line.

Learning letter Dhaal

Look at the arrows. Trace each letter in the direction of the arrow. Then put a dot above the letter. Next, write the letter on the blank lines. Note, the letter Dhaal is written above the red dashed line.

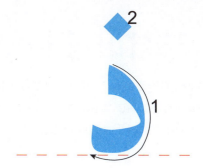

Learning letter Raa

Look at the arrows. Trace each letter in the direction of the arrow. Next, write the letter on the blank lines. Note, the letter Raa is written in the middle of the red dashed line.

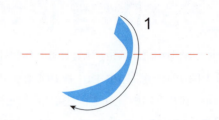

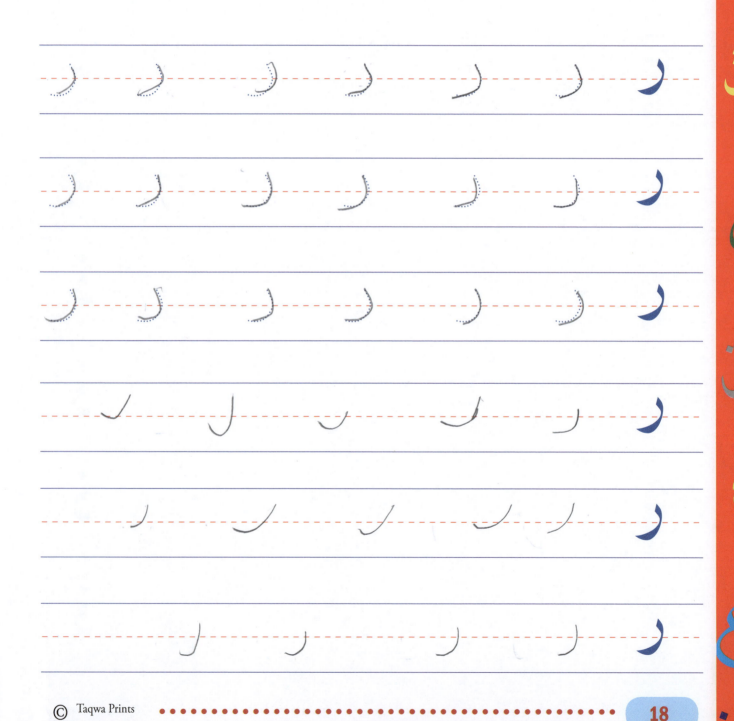

Learning letter Zaa

Look at the arrows. Trace each letter in the direction of the arrow. Then put a dot above the letter. Next, write the letter on the blank lines. Note, the letter Zaa is written in the middle of the red dashed line.

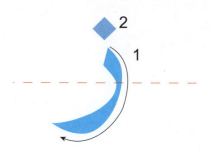

Learning letter Zaa

Practice letters

ث

ج

ح

خ

د

ذ

ر

ز

ع ط

ن

ث

خ غ

ق

ى

ه

م

Learning letter Seen

Look at the arrows. Trace each letter in the direction of the arrow, starting with number 1 arrow and continuing with number 2 and so on. Next, write the letter on the blank lines. Note, the letter Seen is written in the middle of the red dashed line.

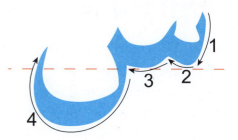

Learning letter Sheen

Look at the arrows. Trace each letter in the direction of the arrow, starting with number 1 arrow and continuing with number 2 and so on. Then put three dots above the letter. Next, write the letter on the blank lines. Note, the letter Sheen is written in the middle of the red dashed line.

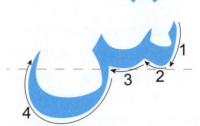

Learning letter Saad

Look at the arrows. Trace each letter in the direction of the arrow, starting with number 1 arrow and continuing with number 2 and so on. Next, write the letter on the blank lines. Note, the letter Saad is written in the middle of the red dashed line.

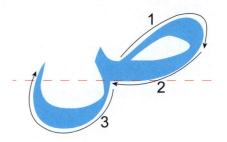

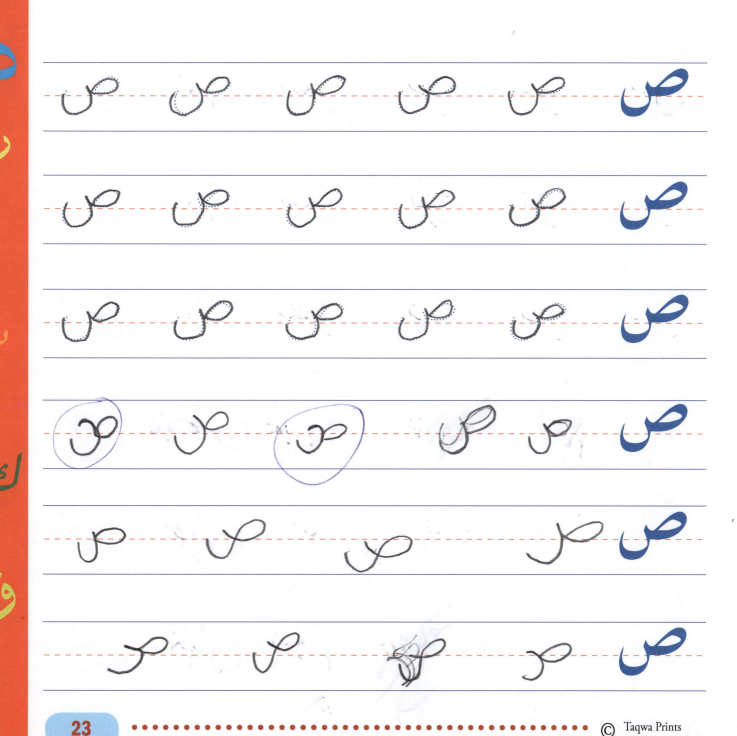

•••••••••••••••••••••••••••••••••• © Taqwa Prints

Learning letter Daad

Look at the arrows. Trace each letter in the direction of the arrow, starting with number 1 arrow and continuing with number 2 and so on. Then put a dot above the letter. Next, write the letter on the blank lines. Note, the letter Daad is written in the middle of the red dashed line.

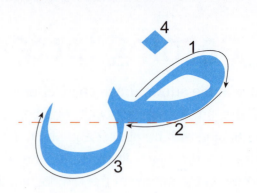

Learning letter Toa

Look at the arrows. Trace each letter in the direction of the arrow, starting with number 1 arrow and continuing with number 2 and so on. Next, write the letter on the blank lines. Note, the letter Toa is written above the red dashed line.

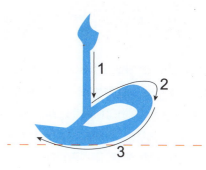

Learning letter Zoa

Look at the arrows. Trace each letter in the direction of the arrow, starting with number 1 arrow and continuing with number 2 and so on. Then put a dot above the letter. Next, write the letter on the blank lines. Note, the letter Zoa is written above the red dashed line.

ظ

alisha

ظ   ظ   ظ   ظ   ظ   ظ   ظ

ظ   ظ   ظ   ظ   ظ   ظ   ظ

ظ   ظ   ظ   ظ   ظ   ظ   ظ

ظ   ظ   ظ   ظ   ظ   ظ   ظ

ظ   ظ   ظ   ظ   ظ   ظ   ظ

ظ   ظ   ظ   ظ   ظ   ظ

Practice letters

ر   ر   ر   ر   ر

ز   زَ   زْ   زَ   زْ

س   س   س   س   س

ش   ش   ش   ش   ش

ص   ص   ص   ص   ص

ض   ض   ض   ض   ض

ط   ط   ط   ط   ط

ظ   ظ   ظ   ظ   ظ

Learning letter Ain

Look at the arrows. Trace each letter in the direction of the arrow, starting with number 1 arrow and continuing with number 2 and so on. Next, write the letter on the blank lines. Note, the letter Ain is written in the middle of the red dashed line as shown.

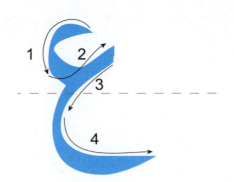

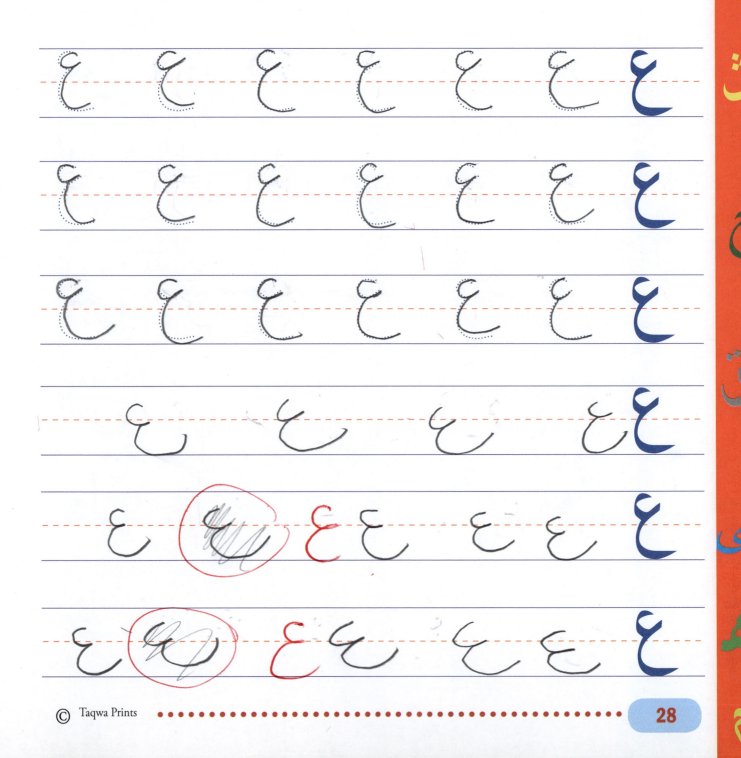

© Taqwa Prints

28

Learning letter Ghayn

Look at the arrows. Trace each letter in the direction of the arrow, starting with number 1 arrow and continuing with number 2 and so on. Then put a dot above the letter. Next, write the letter on the blank lines. Note, the letter Ghayn is written in the middle of the red dashed line as shown.

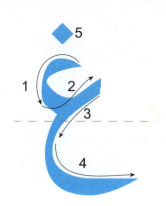

Learning letter Faa

Look at the arrows. Trace each letter in the direction of the arrow, starting with number 1 arrow and continuing with number 2 and so on. Then put a dot above the letter. Next, write the letter on the blank lines. Note, the letter Faa is written above the red dashed line.

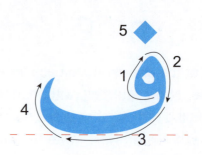

Learning letter Qaaf

Look at the arrows. Trace each letter in the direction of the arrow, starting with number 1 arrow and continuing with number 2 and so on. Then put two dots above the letter. Next, write the letter on the blank lines. Note, the letter Qaaf is written in the middle of the red dashed line as shown.

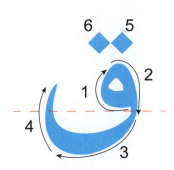

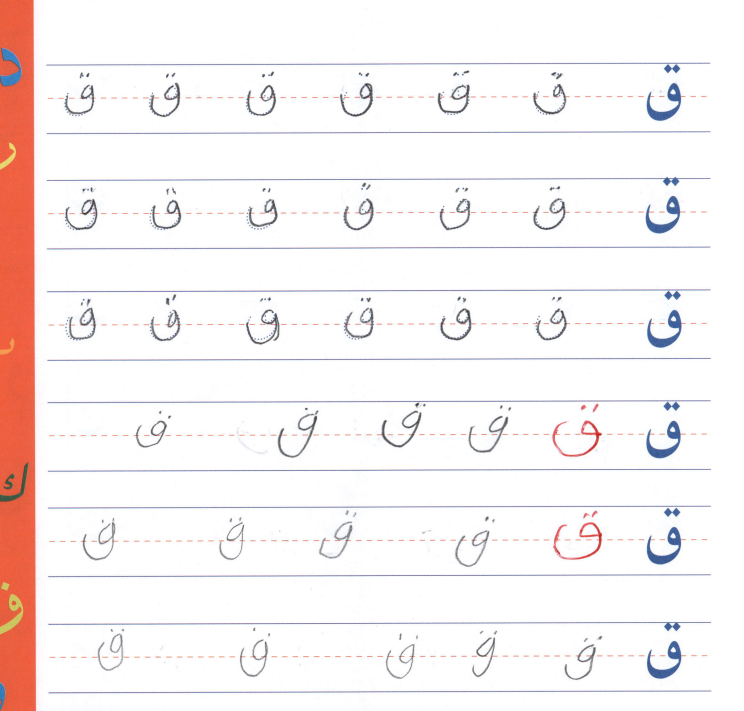

Learning letter Kaaf

Look at the arrows. Trace each letter in the direction of the arrow, starting with number 1 arrow and continuing with number 2 and so on. Then put a curvy "S" in the middle of the letter. Next, write the letter on the blank lines. Note, the letter Kaaf is written above the red dashed line.

3 - 4

ض

ط

ظ

ع

غ

ف

ق

ك

© Taqwa Prints

Learning letter Laam

Look at the arrows. Trace each letter in the direction of the arrow, starting with number 1 arrow and continuing with number 2. Next, write the letter on the blank lines. Note, the letter Laam is written slighly below the red dashed line.

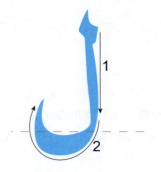

Learning letter Meem

Look at the arrows. Trace each letter in the direction of the arrow, starting with number 1 arrow and continuing with number 2 and so on. Next, write the letter on the blank lines. Note, the letter Meem is written in the middle of the red dashed line.

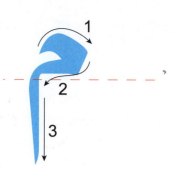

Learning letter Noon

Look at the arrows. Trace each letter in the direction of the arrow, starting with number 1 arrow and continuing with number 2. Then put a dot in the middle. Next, write the letter on the blank lines. Note, the letter Noon is written slighly below the red dashed line.

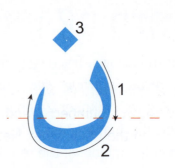

Learning letter Haa

Look at the arrows. Trace each letter in the direction of the arrow, starting with number 1 arrow and continuing with number 2 and so on. Next, write the letter on the blank lines. Note, the letter Haa is written above the red dashed line.

 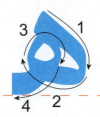

Learning letter Waaw

Look at the arrows. Trace each letter in the direction of the arrow, starting with number 1 arrow and continuing with number 2 and so on. Next, write the letter on the blank lines. Note, the letter Waaw is written in the middle of the red dashed line.

Learning letter Yaa

Look at the arrows. Trace each letter in the direction of the arrow, starting with number 1 arrow and continuing with number 2 and so on. Then put two dots below the letter. Next, write the letter on the blank lines. Note, the letter Yaa is written in the middle of the red dashed line.

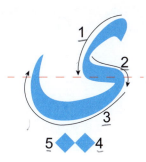

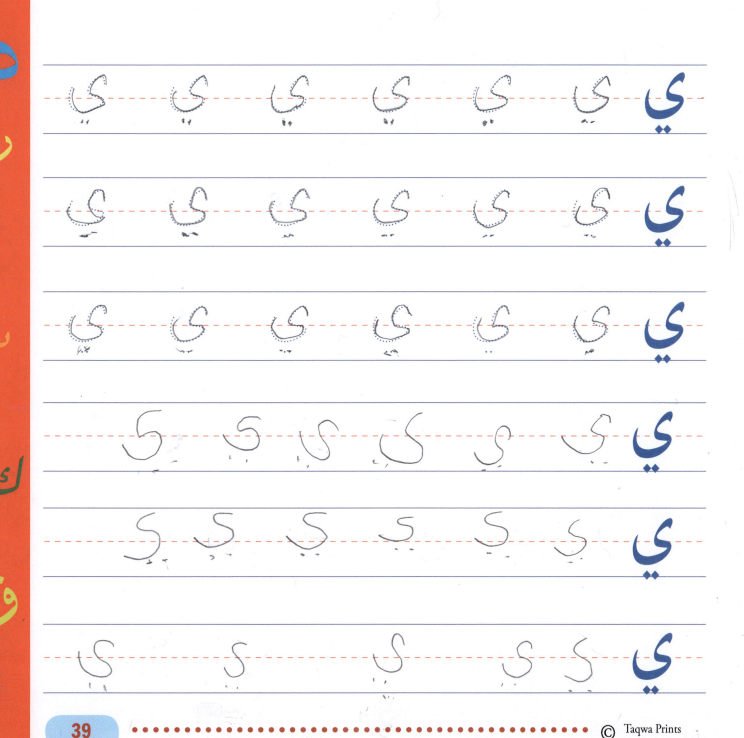

Practice letters

ق

ك

ل

م

ن

ه

و

ي

ط ع ن ث خ ق ى ه م

40

Practice with moon letters

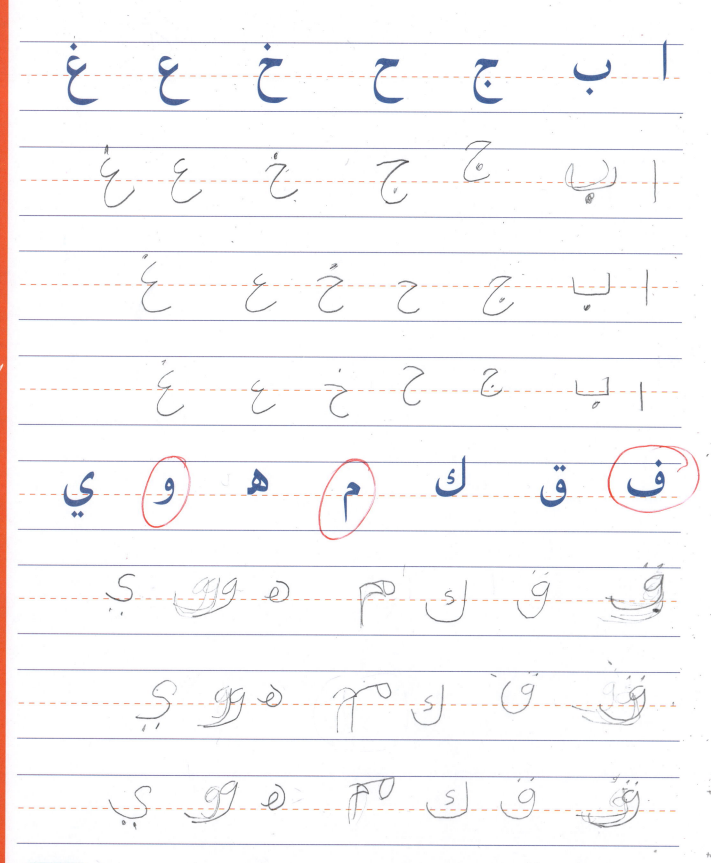

Taqwa Prints

Practice with sun letters

Practice with joining letters

Until this point, we learned writing individual Arabic letters. When these letters are written to form a word or a sentence, they are written in a joined-up form. The shapes of many of the letters change as they join with the alphabet before it or after it. Many a times, the same letter changes its shape depending upon whether it is used in the beginning, middle or end of a word. In English writing we do not see such changes in the shapes of letters.

We must, therefore, learn and practice the different forms of the Arabic alphabets so that we can read the words and sentences. Also, in Arabic, the vowel marks are used to facilitate reading. We will learn the vowel marks later in this workbook.

Each letter has four forms. These forms are: the letter by itself, beginning-, middle- and end-shapes. Below is a table showing the examples of the four forms. Note that some letters do not have a middle form.

Practice writing the forms   Examples of four forms

End	Middle	Beginning	End	Middle	Beginning	By itself
			ﺎ	No middle form, because it cannot attach with a letter after it.	أ	أ
			ـﺐ	ـﺒـ	ﺑ	ب
			ـﺖ	ـﺘـ	ﺗ	ت
			ـﺔ			ة
			ـﺚ	ـﺜـ	ﺛ	ث
			ـﺞ	ـﺠـ	ﺟ	ج
			ـﺢ	ـﺤـ	ﺣ	ح

Practice writing the forms

Examples of four forms

End	Middle	Beginning	End	Middle	Beginning	By itself
			خ	ﺨ	ﺧ	خ
			ﺪ	No middle form, because it cannot attach with a letter after it.	د	د
			ﺬ	No middle form, because it cannot attach with a letter after it.	ذ	ذ
			ﺮ	No middle form, because it cannot attach with a letter after it.	ر	ر
			ﺰ	No middle form, because it cannot attach with a letter after it.	ز	ز
			ﺲ	ﺴ	ﺳ	س
			ﺶ	ﺸ	ﺷ	ش
			ﺺ	ﺼ	ﺻ	ص
			ﺾ	ﻀ	ﺿ	ض
			ﻂ	ﻄ	ﻃ	ط
			ﻆ	ﻈ	ﻇ	ظ
			ﻊ	ﻌ	ﻋ	ع
			ﻎ	ﻐ	ﻏ	غ

Practice writing the forms

Examples of four forms

End	Middle	Beginning	End	Middle	Beginning	By itself
			ف	فـ	فـ	ف
			ق	ـقـ	قـ	ق
			ك	ـكـ	كـ	ك
			ل	ـلـ	لـ	ل
			م	ـمـ	مـ	م
			ن	ـنـ	نـ	ن
			ه	ـهـ	هـ	ه
			و	No middle form, because it cannot attach with a letter after it.	و	و
			ي	ـيـ	يـ	ي

Practice with joining letters

Below are a few examples of how the shapes of individual letters change and how they are joined to form a word. Practice writing the joined words in the lines below the examples.

ا + ب + د = ابد = ا بد

ابد

أبد   أبد   أبد

ا + ح + د = احد = احد

احد

أحد   أحد   أحد

ا + س + ر = اسر = اسر

اسر

أسر   أسر   أسر

ا + ك + ل = اكل = اكل

اكل

أكل   أكل   أكل

Practice with joining letters

Below are a few examples of how the shapes of individual letters change and how they are joined to form a word. Practice writing the joined words in the lines below the examples.

ا + م + ر = امـر = امر

امر

امـن = ا + م + ن = امن

امن

ا + خ + ر = اخـر = اخر

اخر

ا + ف + ل = افـل = افل

افل

Practice with joining letters

Below are a few examples of how the shapes of individual letters change and how they are joined to form a word. Practice writing the joined words in the lines below the examples.

بتل ‏ بتل = ب ـتـل = ل + ت + ب

بتل ‏ ‏ بنل ‏ ‏ بنل ‏ ‏ بنل

بدع ‏ ‏ بدع = بـدع = ع + د + ب

بدع ‏ ‏ بلع ‏ ‏ بلع ‏ ‏ بلع

برك ‏ ‏ برك = بـرك = ك + ر + ب

برك ‏ ‏ برك ‏ ‏ برك ‏ ‏ برك

بعث ‏ ‏ بعث = بعث = ث + ع + ب

بعث ‏ ‏ بعث ‏ ‏ بعث ‏ ‏ بعث

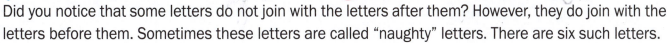

Practice with "naughty" letters

Did you notice that some letters do not join with the letters after them? However, they do join with the letters before them. Sometimes these letters are called "naughty" letters. There are six such letters.

ا د د ذ ذ ر ر ز ز و

In this example, the first letter ا does not join with the letter after it.

ا م ر

The first letter ا does not join with the letter after it. But as can be seen below, it joins with letter before it.

ا + ب = اب

ب + ا = با	س + ا = سا	ج + ا = جا

More examples:

ب + د = بد	س + ر = سر	ر + س = رس
د + ب = دب	ب + د = بد	ز + ت = تز
ق + ذ = قذ	ذ + ق = ذق	و + ظ = ظو
ا + ل = ال	و + ي = يو	ش + ر = شر

Practice with "naughty" letters

When two "naughty" letters appear side by side, they do not join with each other.

و   ز   ر   ذ   د   ا

Two "naughty" letters do not join with each other.

دا = ا + د   اد = د + ا

More examples:

ذو = و + ذ   ذا = ا + ذ

ود = د + و   در = ر + د

زد = د + ز   زر = ر + ز

رد = د + ر   رو = ر + ر

ار = ر + ا   دا = ا + د

وز = ز + و   در = ر + د

Practice with joining letters

ا + ن + ت = انت = انت

انت

ا + ث + ر = اثر = اثر

اثر

ا + ر + ب = ارب = ارب

ارب

ا + ف + ق = افق = افق

افق

© Taqwa Prints

Practice with joining letters

ا + م + د = ا م د = امد

امد

ا + م + ل = ا م ل = امل

امل

ا + ه + ل = ا ه ل = اهل

اهل

ا + د + م = ا د م = ادم

ادم

ي ث ش ك ن ط م ف ح

Practice with joining letters

ب + ل + د = بلد = بلد

بلد

ب + خ + ل = بخل = بخل

بخل

ب + س + ط = بسط = بسط

بسط

ب + ص + ر = بصر = بصر

بصر

Practice with joining letters

ع + ب + س = عـبـس = عبس

عبس

ط + ب + ق = طـبـق = طبق

طبق

س + ب + ح = سـبـح = سبح

سبح

ط + ا + ب = طـاب = طاب

طاب

Practice with joining letters

ت + ج + ر = تجر = تجر

تجر

ق + ت + ل = قتل = قتل

قتل

م + ت + ع = متع = متع

متع

ث + ب + ت = ثبت = ثبت

ثبت

Practice with joining letters

ت + ق + ن = تـقـن = تقن

تقن

ر + ت + ق = ر تـق = رتق

رتق

ف + ت + ح = فـتـح = فتح

فتح

س + ك + ت = سـكـت = سكت

سكت

Practice with joining letters

ث ث ث ث

ث + م + ر = ثمر = ثمر

ثمر

د + ث + ر = د ثر = دثر

دثر

ك + ث + ر = كثر = كثر

كثر

ل + ب + ث = لبث = لبث

لبث

Practice with joining letters

غ + ا + ث = غـاث = غاث

غاث

ع + ب + ث = عـبـث = عبث

عبث

ح + ن + ث = حـنـث = حنث

حنث

ح + د + ث = حـد ث = حدث

حدث

Practice with joining letters

ج + ن + ب = جــنـب = جنب

جنب

س + ج + د = ســجـد = سجد

سجد

و + ج + د = وجـد = وجد

وجد

خ + ر + ج = خــرج = خرج

خرج

© Taqwa Prints

Practice with joining letters

| ج ج ج |

ج + ذ + ع = جـذع = جذع

جذع

ع + ج + ب = عـجـب = عجب

عجب

ف + ج + ر = فـجـر = فجر

فجر

ش + ج + ر = شـجـر = شجر

شجر

ي
ث
ش
م
ك
ن
ط
م
ف
ع

Practice with joining letters

ح حـ ـحـ ـح

ح + ا + د = حـاد = حاد

حاد

ح + ن + د = حـنـد = حند

حند

ن + ح + ل = نـحـل = نحل

نحل

س + ا + ح = سـاح = ساح

ساح

Practice with joining letters

ح   حـ   ـحـ   ـح

ح + ت + م = حـتـم = حتم

حتم

ص + ا + ح + ب = صاحب = صاحب

صاحب

س + ح + ق = سـحـق = سحق

سحق

ص + ا + ح = صـاح = صاح

صاح

Practice with vowels

Now that we learned the letters and their short forms, it is a good time to learn the vowel marks. The vowel marks help us pronounce an Arabic word correctly. All the vowel signs are written above or below Arabic letters. After we learn the vowel marks, we will practice writing words with the marks.

و Damma   ╱ Fatha

╱ Kasra

> All the vowels are written above or below the Arabic letter.

حَ جَ ثَ تَ بَ اَ

> Fatha is a short angular stroke written ABOVE an Arabic letter. It is pronounced as "a" as in English word "bat".

حِ جِ ثِ تِ بِ اِ

> Kasra is a short angular stroke written BELOW an Arabic letter. It is pronounced as "i" as in English word "sit".

حُ جُ ثُ تُ بُ اُ

> Damma is a short loop-like stroke written ABOVE an Arabic letter. It is pronounced as "u" as in English word "pull".

اَ اِ اُ بُ بِ بَ تُ تَ تِ ثُ ثَ ثِ

جَ جِ جُ حَ حِ حُ خَ خِ خُ دَ دِ دُ

ذَ ذِ ذُ رَ رِ رُ زَ زِ زُ سَ سِ سُ

شَ شِ شُ صَ صِ صُ ضَ ضِ ضُ

Practice with vowels

The vowel marks help us pronounce an Arabic word correctly. All the vowel signs are written above or below Arabic letters. After we learn the vowel marks, we will practice writing words with the marks.

وُ Damma	َ Fatha	All the vowels are written above or below the Arabic letter.
	ِ Kasra	

غُ غَ غِ غُ   عَ عِ عُ   ظُ ظِ ظَ   طَ طِ طُ

فَ فِ فُ   قَ قِ قُ   كَ كِ كُ   لَ لِ لُ

مُ مَ مِ   نَ نِ نُ   هَ هِ هُ

يَ يِ يُ   وَ وِ وُ

Practice with joining letters

خ خـ ـخـ ـخ

خَ + ب + رَ = خَـبَـرَ = خَبَرَ

خَبَرَ

خَ + بُ + ث = خَـبُـث = خُبُث

خَبُثَ

بَ + خِ + لَ = بَـخِـلَ = بَخِلَ

بَخِلَ

رَ + خِ + يَ = رَخِيَ = رَخِيَ

رَخِيَ

Practice with joining letters

سَخِطَ = سَخِطَ = طَ + خِ + سَ

سَخِطَ

خَلَفَ = خَلَفَ = فَ + لَ + خَ

خَلَفَ

خَلَ = خَلَ = لَ + خَ

خَلَ

فَخَرَ = فَخَرَ = رَ + خَ + فَ

فَخَرَ

Practice with joining letters

د لـ د لـ

دَ + رَّ + جَ = دَرَّجَ

دَرَّجَ

دَ + خَ + لَ = دَ خَلَ = دَ خَلَ

دَ خَلَ

صَ + دَ + قَ = صَـدَ قَ = صَدَ قَ

صَـدَ قَ

نَ + ا + دَ + ى = نَـا دَى = نَادَى

نَادَى

Practice with joining letters

د	د	لـ	لـ

غَ + دَ + ا = غَـدَا = غَدَا

غَدَا

غَ + دَ + رَ = غَـدَرَ = غَدَر

غَدَرَ

فَ + رَ + دَ = فَـرَدَ = فَرَد

فَرَدَ

مَ + سَ + دَ = مَـسَـدَ = مَسَد

مَسَدَ

Practice with joining letters

ذ   ذ   ذ

ن + ف + ذَ = نَفَذَ = نَفَذَ

نَفَذَ

ذُ + بِ + حَ = ذُبِحَ = ذُبِحَ

ذُبِحَ

عَ + ذُ + ب = عَذُبَ = عَذُب

عَذُب

ن + ذَ + رَ = نَذَرَ = نَذَر

نَذَرَ

69 ●   © Taqwa Prints

Practice with joining letters

أَ + ذِ + نَ = أَ ذِ نَ

أَ ذِ نَ

أَ + ذِ + نَ + تَ = أَ ذِ نَ تَ = أَ ذِ نَ تَ

أَ ذِ نَ تَ

يُ + ب + ذَ + رَ = يُ بـ ذَ رَ = يُبذَرَ

يُبذَرَ

جَ + ذَ + عَ = جَ ذَ عَ = جَذَعَ

جَذَعَ

Practice with joining letters

ر   ر   ر   ر

رَ + بِ + حَ = رَ بِ حَ = رَبِحَ

رَبِحَ

بَ + رَ + كَ = بَ رَ كَ = بَرَكَ

بَرَكَ

شَ + رِ + كَ = شَ رِ كَ = شَرِكَ

شَرِكَ

مَ + رْ + يَ + مْ = مَرْيَمْ = مَرْيَمْ

مَرْيَمْ

Practice with joining letters

رۡ رۡ رۡ رۡ رۡ

اَ + رَ + مَ = اَرَمَ

اَرَمَ

جَ + رَ + مَ = جَ رَ مَ = جَرَمَ

جَرَمَ

جَ + هَ + رَ = جَ هَ رَ = جَهَر

جَهَر

عَ + رَ + جَ = عَ رَ جَ = عَرَجَ

عَرَجَ

Practice with joining letters

ز ز ز ز

زَ + هَ + دَ = زَ هَ دَ = زَهَدَ

زَهَدَ

عَ + زَ + بَ = عَ زَ بَ = عَزَبَ

عَزَبَ

مَ + زَ + ق = مَ زَ ق = مَزَق

مَزَق

زَ + كَ + ي = زَكَي = زَكَي

زَكَي

73 ······························· © Taqwa Prints

Practice with joining letters

زَ + اَ + لَ = زَاَلَ

زَاَلَ

نَ + زَ + لَ = نَزَلَ = نَزَلَ

نَزَلَ

مَ + عَ + زَ + لَ = مَعـزَلَ = مَعزَلَ

مَعزَلَ

نَ + زَ + رَ = نَزَرَ = نَزَرَ

نَزَرَ

• • • • • • • • • • • 74

Practice with joining letters

سَ + لِ + مَ = سَ لِ مَ = سَلِمَ

سَلِمَ

وَ + سَ + لَ = وَ سَ لَ = وَسَلَ

وَسَلَ

رَ + سُ + و + لَ = رَ سُ و لَ = رَسُولَ

رَسُولَ

بَ + سَ + طَ = بَ سَ طَ = بَسَطَ

بَسَطَ

Practice with joining letters

س ‍س‍ ‍سـ ‍س

ت َ + سَ + عَ = تَسَعَ = تَسَعَ

تَسَعَ

قَ + سَ + رَ = قَسَرَ = قَسَرَ

قَسَرَ

نَ + سَ + ا + ءَ = نَسَاءَ = نَسَاءَ

نَسَاءَ

كَ + سَ + بَ = كَسَبَ = كَسَبَ

كَسَبَ

ز ش م ث ط ث ك ح

Practice with joining letters

شَ + رِ + كَ = شَرِكَ = شَرِكَ

شَرِكَ

بَ + شَ + رَ = بَشَرَ = بَشَر

بَشَر

كَ + شَ + فَ = كَشَفَ = كَشَفَ

كَشَفَ

فَ + رَ + ش = فَرَش = فَرَش

فَرَش

77 ••••••••••••••••••••••••••••• © Taqwa Prints

Practice with joining letters

شَ + بْ + هَ = شَـبْـهَ = شَبْهَ

شَبْهَ

بَ + طَ + شَ = بَـطَـشَ = بَطَشَ

بَطَشَ

غَ + شِ + يَ = غَـشِـيَ = غَشِيَ

غَشِيَ

عَ + ا + شَ = عَـا شَ = عَاشَ

عَاشَ

Practice with joining letters

صَ + بْ + حَ = صَبْحَ = صبح

صَبْحَ

رَ + صْ + دَ = رَصْدَ = رصد

رَصْدَ

نَ + صْ + رَ = نَصْرَ = نصر

نَصْرَ

اَ + بْ + رَ + صْ = اَبْرَصْ = ابرص

اَبْرَصْ

Practice with joining letters

ص صـ ـصـ ـص

صَ + مَ + دَ = صَمَدَ = صَمَدَ

صَمَدَ

صَ + غِ + رَ = صَغِرَ = صَغِرَ

صَغِرَ

عَ + صَ + ا = عَصَا = عَصَا

عَصَا

بَ + صَ + رَ = بَصَرَ = بَصَرَ

بَصَرَ

ي ث ش ك ن ط م ف ع

© Taqwa Prints · · · · · · · · · · · · · · · · 80

Practice with joining letters

ض ض ض ض

ضَ + بَ + حَ = ضَبَحَ = ضَبَحَ

ضَبَحَ

ضَ + مَ + رَ = ضَمَرَ = ضَمَرَ

ضَمَرَ

بَ + ضَ + عَ = بَضَعَ = بَضَعَ

بَضَعَ

عَ + رَ + ضَ = عَرَضَ = عَرَضَ

عَرَضَ

Practice with joining letters

ض ض ض ض

حَ + ضَ + رُ = حَ ضَ رُ = حَضَرُ

حَضَرُ

ضَ + جَ + عَ = ضَ جَ عَ = ضَجَعَ

ضَجَعَ

خَ + فَ + ضَ = خَ فَ ضَ = خَفَضَ

خَفَضَ

وَ + فَ + ضَ = وَ فَ ضَ = وَفَضَ

وَفَضَ

Practice with joining letters

طُ طَ طُ طَ

طَ + رُ + وَ = طَرُوَ = طَرُو

طَرُو

ح + طَ + م = حَطَم = حَطَم

حَطَم

عَ + طَ + فَ = عَطَفَ = عَطَف

عَطَف

رَ + بَ + طَ = رَبَطَ = رَبَط

رَبَط

Practice with joining letters © Taqwa Prints

Practice with joining letters

$$ ط \quad ط \quad ط \quad ط $$

عَطِل = عَـطِـلَ = لَ + طِ + عَ

عَطِلَ

مَطَر = مَـطَـرَ = رَ + طَ + مَ

مَطَرَ

بَطَل = بَـطَـلَ = لَ + طَ + بَ

بَطَلَ

قَنِط = قَـنِـطَ = طَ + نِ + قَ

قَنِطَ

Practice with joining letters

ظ ظ ظ ظ

ظَ + عَ + نَ = ظَعَنَ = ظَعَنَ

ظَعَنَ

ظَ + لَ + مَ = ظَلَمَ = ظَلَمَ

ظَلَمَ

عَ + ظَ + مَ = عَظَمَ = عَظَمَ

عَظَمَ

كَ + ظَ + مَ = كَظَمَ = كَظَمَ

كَظَمَ

Practice with joining letters

ظ ظ ظ ظ

ظَ + نَ + نَ + ا = ظَنَنَا = ظَنَنَا

ظَنَنَا

ظَ + فَ + رَ = ظَفَرَ = ظَفَر

ظَفَرَ

اَ + ظَ + هَ + رَ = اَظْهَرَ = اَظْهَر

اَظْهَرَ

غَ + لَ + ظَ = غَلَظَ = غَلَظَ

غَلَظَ

Practice with joining letters

عـ عـ ـﻌ ع

عَ + ن = عَن = عَن

عَن

عَ + ا + لَ = عَالَ = عَالَ

عَالَ

فَ + عَ + لَ = فَعَلَ = فَعَلَ

فَعَلَ

نَ + عَ + مَ + ة = نَعمَة = نَعمَة

نَعمَة

Practice with joining letters

عـ ـعـ ع

وَ + عَ + دَ = وَعَدَ = وَعَدَ

وَعَدَ

قَ + رَ + عَ = قَرَعَ = قَرَعَ

قَرَعَ

عَ + شَ + رَ = عَشَرَ = عَشَرَ

عَشَرَ

جَ + عَ + لَ = جَعَلَ = جَعَلَ

جَعَلَ

Practice with joining letters

غ غ غ غ

غَ + ا + رَ = غَارَ = غَارَ

غَارَ

لَ + غَ + ب = لَغَبَ = لَغَبَ

لَغَبَ

لَ + غَ + يَ = لَغَيَ = لَغَيَ

لَغَي

نَ + زَ + غَ = نَزَغَ = نَزَغَ

نَزَغَ

Practice with joining letters

غ + ا + د = غَاد = غَاد

غَاد

غ + نِ + م = غَنِم = غَنِم

غَنِم

دَ + م + غ = دَمَغ = دَمَغ

دَمَغ

غَ + رِ + م = غَرِم = غَرِم

غَرِم

• **90**

Practice with joining letters

ف ف ف ف

فَسَخَ = فَسَخَ = خَ + سَ + فَ

فَسَخَ

وَفَرَ = وَفَرَ = رَ + فَ + وَ

وَفَر

شَفَعَ = شَفَعَ = عَ + فَ + شَ

شَفَعَ

كَسَفَ = كَسَفَ = فَ + سَ + كَ

كَسَفَ

·········· © Taqwa Prints

Practice with joining letters

فَ + رِ + ةً = فَرِةً = فَرِةً

فَرِةً

نَ + فَ + شً = نَفَشً = نَفَشً

نَفَشً

سَ + فَ + رً = سَفَرً = سَفَرً

سَفَرً

قَ + فَ + لً = قَفَلً = قَفَلً

قَفَلً

Practice with joining letters

ق   ﻗ   ﻗ   ق

قَ + ا + سَ = قَ ا سَ = قَاسَ

قَاسَ

قَ + د = قَد = قَد

قَد

قَ + ل + م = قَلم = قَلم

قَلم

فَ + لَ + ق = فَلَق = فَلَق

فَلَق

Practice with joining letters

قَ + ل + ب = قَـلـب = قَلب

قَلب

بَ + قِ + ي = بَـقِـي = بَقِي

بَقِي

دَ + ف + قَ = دَ فـقَ = دَ فق

دَ فقَ

سَ + بَ + ق = سَـبَـق = سَبق

سَبق

Practice with joining letters

$$ك \quad ک \quad ک \quad ك$$

كَ + م = كَم = كَم

كَم

كُ + ل = كُل = كُل

كُل

بَ + رَ + كَ = بَرَكَ = بَرَكَ

بَرَكَ

فَ + كَ + رَ = فَكَرَ = فَكَرَ

فَكَرَ

Practice with joining letters

شَ + رِ + كَ = شَرِكَ = شَرِكَ

شَرِكَ

كَ + تَ + بَ = كَتَبَ = كَتَبَ

كَتَبَ

فَ + كَ + رَ = فَكَرَ = فَكَرَ

فَكَرَ

شَ + كَ + ا = شَكَا = شَكَا

شَكَا

Practice with joining letters

ل ل ل

لَ + ي + ل + ة = لَيلَة = لَيلَة

لَيلَة

ظَ + لَ + م = ظَلَم = ظَلَم

ظَلَم

قَ + لَ + دَ = قَلَدَ = قَلَدَ

قَلَدَ

بَ + خ + لَ = بَخِلَ = بَخِلَ

بَخِلَ

Practice with joining letters

ل   ل   لـ

سَ + لَ + م = سَلَم = سَلَم

سَلَم

فَ + لَ + ق = فَلَق = فَلَق

فَلَق

نَ + زَ + لَ = نَزَلَ = نَزَلَ

نَزَلَ

زَ + ا + لَ = زَالَ

زَالَ

Practice with joining letters

م م م م

مِ + ن = مِن = مِن = مِن

مِن

لَ + م = لَم = لَم = لَم

لَم

حَ + سَ + م = حَسَم = حَسَم = حَسَم

حَسَم

مَ + ر + ي + م = مَريَم = مَريَم = مَريَم

مَريَم

Practice with joining letters

م   مـ   ـمـ   ـم

حَ + ا + م = حَـام = حَام

حَام

شَ + م + عَ = شَـمـعَ = شَمعَ

شَمعَ

لَ + جَ + م = لَـجَـم = لَجَم

لَجَم

عِ + مَ + ا + د = عِـمَـا د = عِمَاد

عِمَاد

$$ ن \quad نـ \quad ـنـ \quad ـن $$

$$ نَ + صَ + رَ = نَصَرَ = نَصَر $$

$$ نَصَرَ $$

$$ اَ + ن + اَ = اَناَ = اَ + اَ = اَناَ $$

$$ اَناَ $$

$$ بَ + دَ + ن = بَدَن = بَدَ ن = بَدَن $$

$$ بَدَ ن $$

$$ رَ + كِ + ن = رَكِن = رَ كِ ن = رَكِن $$

$$ رَكِن $$

Practice with joining letters

ن ن ن ن

نَ + فَ + شَ = نَفَشَ = نَفَشَ

نَفَشَ

يَ + مِ + نَ = يَمِنَ = يَمِنَ

يَمِنَ

غَ + بَ + نَ = غَبَنَ = غَبَنَ

غَبَنَ

دَ + هِ + نَ = دَهِنَ = دَهِنَ

دَهِنَ

· · · · · · · · · · · · ·

ي ث ثُ مْ كـ ن طـ مـ فـ عـ

Practice with joining letters

ه هـ ه

هَـ + لَ = هَـلَ = هَل

هَل

هَـ + دَ = هَـدَ = هَد

هَد

وَ + هَـ + نَ = وَهَـنَ = وَهَن

وَهَن

فَ + هِـ + مَ = فَهِـمَ = فَهِم

فَهِـم

Practice with joining letters

هَ + جَ + عْ = هَجَعْ = هَجَعْ

هَجَعْ

هَ + ا + مَ = هَا مَ = هَامَ

هَامَ

بَ + هِ + تَ = بَهِتَ = بَهِتَ

بَهِتَ

جَ + هِ + مَ = جَهِمَ = جَهِمَ

جَهِمَ

Practice with joining letters

وَا = ا + وَ

وَا

وَاَجِب = وَاَجِب = ب + جِ + اَ + وَ

وَاَجِب

لَوَن = لَوَن = ن + وَ + لَ

لَوَن

رُوم = رُوم = م + و + رُ

رُوم

Practice with joining letters

و   و   و

سَ + وِ + يَ = سَوِيَ = سَوِيَ

سَوِيَ

غَ + وَ + يَ = غَوَيَ = غَوَيَ

غَوَيَ

فَ + وْ + عَ + ة = فَوْعَة = فَوْعَة

فَوْعَة

وَ + هَ + نَ = وَهَنَ = وَهَنَ

وَهَنَ

Practice with joining letters

 يَ + دَ + ى = يَدَى = يَدَى

يَدَى

ي + و + سُ + ف = يُوسُف = يُوسُف

يُوسُف

حَ + يَ + ا + ة = حَيَاة = حَيَاة

حَيَاة

رَ + هِ + ي + ف = رَهِيف = رَهِيف

رَهِيف

Practice with joining letters

ي يـ ـيـ ـي

لَ + ي + سَ = لَـيـسَ = لَيسَ

لَيسَ

يَ + مَ + ن = يَـمَـن = يَمَن

يَمَن

يَ + و + م = يَـومَ = يَوم

يَوم

مُ + جِ + ي + د = مُـجِـيـد = مُجِيد

مُجِيد

Practice with vowels: tanween

Let us now learn some other forms of vowel marks. The Arabic vowel marks fatha, kasra, and damma are sometimes doubled. When doubled, they are known as tanween. When tanween is used, the sound of the vowel mark changes.

	بَا	تَا	تَا	=

> **Fathataan:** It is two fatha signs above a letter. It is pronounced as "an". It is usually supported by an alif.

	ب	ت	ت	=

> **Kasrataan:** It is two kasra signs below a letter. It is pronounced as "in".

> **Dammataan:** It is two damma signs above a letter. It is pronounced as "un".
>
> Sometimes it is written as two damma
>
> Sometimes it is written as: or

أ أ آ بِ بِ بُ تٍ تٍ تُ تٌ تٍ تٌ

جً جٍ جُ حً حٍ حُ خً خٍ خُ دً دٍ دُ

ذً ذٍ ذُ رً رٍ رُ زً زٍ زُ سً سٍ سُ

شً شٍ شُ صً صٍ صُ ضً ضٍ ضُ

Practice with vowels: tanween

The vowel marks help us pronounce an Arabic word correctly. All the vowel signs are written above or below Arabic letters. After we learn the vowel marks, we will practice writing words with the marks.

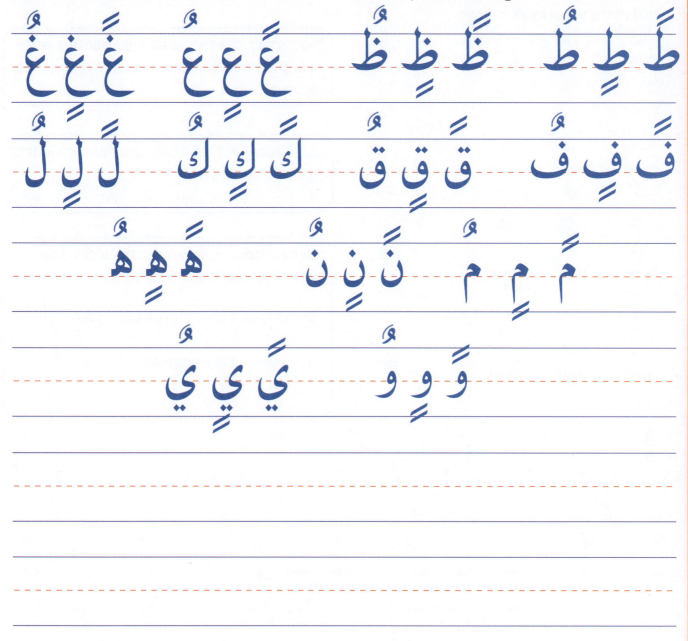

Practice with long vowels

Three Arabic letters are also used to make the sound of the short vowel long. For example, when a fatha sign is followed by an Alif, the sound of fatha is made longer. The "a" sound of fatha now sounds like "aa".

In this example, fatha sign is followed by an alif. The sound of fatha "a" will now become long, like "aa". Ba fatha followed by an alif makes sound of "ba" long - "baa".	اَ بَ بَا
In this example, kasra sign is followed by a ya. The sound of kasra "i" will now become long, like "ee". Ba kasra followed by a ya makes sound of "bi" long - "bee".	رِ بِي رِي
In this example, damma sign is followed by a waaw. The sound of fatha "u" will now become long, like "oo". Ba damma followed by a waaw makes sound of "bu" long - "boo".	رُ بُو وُ
When one alif is followed by another alif, their sound becomes long. The long sound is indicated by a special curved sign placed on top of alif. It is called alif al-madd.	
When lam is followed by an alif, their shape changes. When reading such letter, remember to make long sound "laa".	

آبَ   لاَخَذَ   لاَبِسَ   سِلاَحَ   آنِ   اَلاَ

Practice with sukoon

Sukoon is a sign placed on top of a letter. The sukoon signs used in the Qur'ān and in standard Arabic writing are different. In standard Arabic writing, the sukoon sign is a small circle (◯) placed on top of a letter. It would mean the sound of the letter is shortened. For example, lam becomes "l", kaaf becomes "k" and so on.

However, in the Qur'ān, the sign (◯) would indicate the letter is not pronounced at all. In the Qur'ān, the sukoon sign is a small flat half-circle (ﹾ), which means the sound of the letter is shortened.

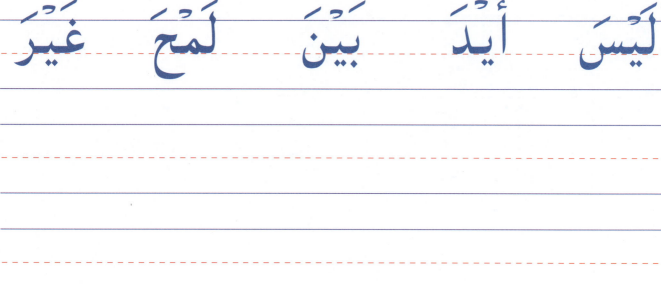

Practice with sukoon

عَيْن خَيْرَة فَوْعَة كَوْكَب زَوْج

Practice with sukoon

لَغْيَ   مَوْجَة   تَوْرَات   سَوْىَ   يَوْمَ

Practice with shadda

Shadda is a sign placed on top of a letter to indicate that the letter is doubled. Unlike in English, the letter itself if not written twice, but the sign indicates double usage. As such the sound of the letter is made stronger. A shadda is used alone or in combination with a short vowel or with a tanween.

Here "b" is doubled. But in Arabic writing, two of the same letters are not written side by side. Instead, a shadda sign is used.

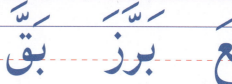

Use of two "ba" is shown. In Arabic writing, two of the same letters are not written side by side. Instead, a shadda sign ( ) is used.

مَنّ   شَرّ   تَخَدُّد   بَقّ   بَرّزَ   اِتَّبَعَ

Practice with all vowel signs

ذَلِكَ الْكِتَبُ لَا رَيْبَ فِيهِ

Practice with all vowel signs

 فَعَّالَ   عَمَّارَ   حِلْيَةً   لَهُمْ ذِكْرًا

Practice with all vowel signs

نَاعِمَةٌ   لِّسَعْيِهَا   فِى جَنَّةٍ عَالِيَةٍ

Practice with all vowel signs

صُمٌّ بُكْمٌ عُمْىٌ فَهُمْ لَا يَرْجِعُونَ

Practice with all vowel signs

لَا يُسْمِنُ وَلَا يُغْنِى مِن جُوعٍ

Practice with all vowel signs

ٱلۡأَكۡبَرُ   ٱلۡعَذَابَ   ٱللَّهُ   فَيُعَذِّبُهُ

Practice with all vowel signs

لَخَبِيرٌ   يَوۡمَئِذٍ   بِهِمۡ   رَبَّهُمۡ   إِنَّ

Practice with all vowel signs

يَسْلُكْهُ رَبِّهِ ذِكْرِ كَفَّارٌ فَاجِرًا اِلَّا

Practice with all vowel signs

إِنَّا أَنزَلْنَهُ فِى لَيْلَةِ الْقَدْرِ

Practice with all vowel signs

لَقَدْ خَلَقْنَا الْإِنسَـٰنَ فِىٓ أَحْسَنِ تَقْوِيمٍ

Practice with all vowel signs

سَبَّحَ لِلّٰهِ مَا فِي أَسْمٰوٰتِ وَٱلْأَرْضِ

Practice with all vowel signs

وَهُوَ بِكُلِّ شَىْءٍ عَلِيمٌ شَىْءٍ قَدِيرٌ

Other useful books for a complete teaching system

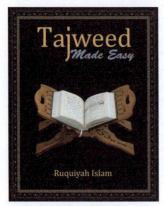

Tajweed Made Easy

100 pages $12.00

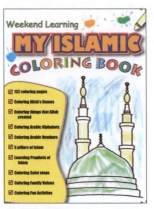

My Islamic Coloring Book

136 pages $10.00

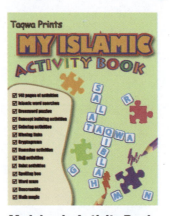

My Islamic Activity Book

160 pages $12.00

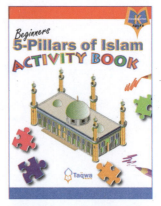

Beginners 5-Pillars of Islam Activity Book

96 pages $10.00

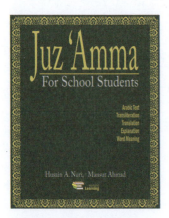

Juz Amma For School Students (with transliteration)

216 pages $13.00

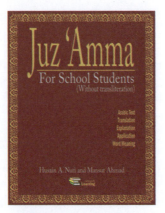

Juz Amma For School Students (without transliteration)

216 pages $13.00

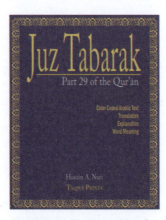

Juz Tabarak: Part 29 of the Qur'ān

200 pages $13.00

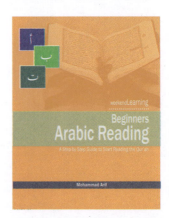

Beginners Arabic Reading

36 pages $6.00

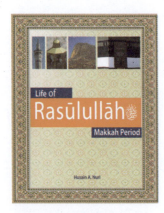

Life of Rasūlullāh (S): Makkah Period

176 pages $13.00

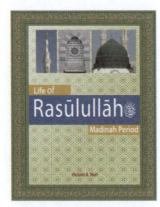

Life of Rasūlullāh (S): Madinah Period

196 pages $13.00

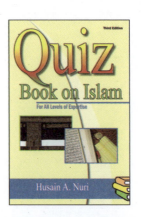

Quiz Book on Islam: For All Levels of Expertise

160 pages $10.00

21-Du'ā for Children

28 pages $2.00